STO

FRIENDS
OF ACPL

W9-CZX-103

JUL 1 '46

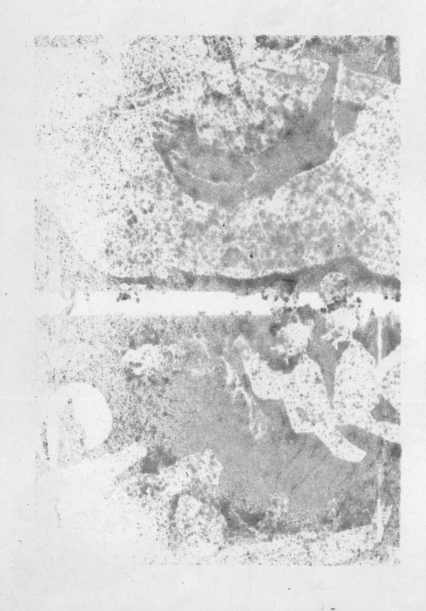

MOTHER GOOSE

ARRANGED AND ILLUSTRATED BY

Roger Duvoisin

MOTHER GOOSE

A COMPREHENSIVE

COLLECTION OF THE RHYMES MADE BY

William Rose Benét

ARRANGED AND ILLUSTRATED BY

Roger Duvoisin

FOR THE HERITAGE PRESS, NEW YORK

The entire contents of this edition are copyright, 1943, by The Heritage Press. MOTHER GOOSE, in the collection made by Mr. Benét and illustrated by Mr. Duvoisin, was first published by The Heritage Press in 1936, then reprinted in 1938, and reprinted again in 1940. This is a new edition, in a fresh format, for which Mr. Duvoisin has made an entirely new set of drawings.

A NOTE on these rhymes : FOR CENTURIES INFANTS

have learned the rhymes of the famous mythical lady who presides over that collection of folk-lore jingle and more modern accretions that now forms the great treasury of the simplest kind of poetry we know. Despite the legend of a Madam Vergoose, founded on the existence of an actual person of that name, it seems now incontrovertible that the first mention of the lady was in French and that her name was attached to a collection of the prose *contes* of Charles Perrault. That was in the *early part* of the Seventeenth Century and the book was called "Contes de ma mère L'Oye." The original "Mother Goose Melody," however, was brought out by John Newbery (whose name is now associated with an annual award in our country for the best children's book of the year) in London about 1760; and then Isaiah Thomas of Worcester, Massachusetts issued the first Mother Goose in America about twenty-five years later.

A few years ago there appeared a delightful book by Katherine Elwes Thomas treating of "The Real Personages of Mother Goose," in which she stated that beyond controversy "the nursery rhymes, largely of Jacobite origin, are political diatribes, religious philippics, and popular street songs, embodying comedies, tragedies, and love episodes of many great historical personages, lavishly interspersed with English and Scotch folklore flung out with dramatic abandon." She traces most absorbingly the origin in British history of rhyme after rhyme.

The present chooser of a certain number of the famous rhymes, with no particular erudition to bring to bear upon the subject, has chosen the contents of the present book merely with reference to those rhymes which have achieved the greatest longevity and are the best known on both sides of the world, in their most popular versions. Naturally this sort of material undergoes, through being committed to memory and transmitted through generations, a number of variations. It was not the present editor's purpose to seek out the absolutely uncorrupted original versions but rather to give the rhymes as they are best known today, or as, through his own memory and knowledge of them, he conceived them to be.

May he, before closing this brief introduction, point out that so good a poet as Oliver Goldsmith may have originally had a finger in the pie, like Little Jack Horner, and that nursery rhymes have not been spurned by recent poets in English, notably Mr. Robert Graves, Mr. Walter de la Mare, and Mr. Ralph Hodgson. These poets in certain work of theirs endeavored to recapture the ingenuous felicities and the spontaneous exuberance of the best of the Mother Goose rhymes, songs, and ballads. For such qualities are by no means to be despised. Any adult who enjoys life and the good things thereof can take proper pleasure in such a brevity as one which is not included here for reasons of space:

> *Round about, round about,*
> *Gooseberry Pie,*
> *My father loves good ale*
> *And so do I!*

I leave you to the most famous of gooseberry pies, merely paying, in conclusion, my delighted respects to the art of the illustrator of this book who, it seems to me, has brought an altogether fresh manner and style to the interpretation of those undying rhymes which, after all their nonsense, contain such treasurable pictures for the mind, and such queer, shrewd wisdom too.

WILLIAM ROSE BENÉT

SEP 9 1946

594544

SING A SONG OF SIXPENCE

Sing a song of sixpence,
  A pocket full of rye;
Four and twenty blackbirds
  Baked in a pie;

When the pie was opened,
  The birds began to sing;
Was not that a dainty dish
  To set before the king?

The king was in the parlor,
  Counting out his money;
The queen was in the kitchen,
  Eating bread and honey;

The maid was in the garden,
  Hanging out the clothes;
Along came a little blackbird,
  And nipped off her nose.

She went to the joiner's
   To buy him a coffin,
But when she came back
   The poor Dog was laughing.

She took a clean dish
   To get him some tripe,
But when she came back
   He was smoking a pipe.

OLD MOTHER HUBBARD

Old Mother Hubbard
Went to the cupboard,
   To get her poor Dog a bone;
But when she came there
The cupboard was bare,
   And so the poor Dog had none.

She went to the fruiterer's
   To buy him some fruit,
But when she came back
   He was playing the flute.

She went to the baker's
   To buy him some bread,
But when she came back
   The poor Dog was dead.

She went to the tailor's
   To buy him a coat,
But when she came back
   He was riding a goat.

She went to the barber's
  To buy him a wig,
But when she came back
  He was dancing a jig.

She went to the tavern
  For white wine and red,
But when she came back
  The Dog stood on his head.

She went to the cobbler's
  To buy him some shoes,
But when she came back
  He was reading the news.

She went to the hosier's
  To buy him some hose,
But when she came back
  He was dressed in his clothes.

This wonderful Dog
  Was Dame Hubbard's delight;
He could sing, he could dance,
  He could read, he could write.

She gave him rich dainties
  Whenever he fed,
And erected a monument
  When he was dead.

LITTLE BETTY WINCKLE

Little Betty Winckle she had a pig,
  It was a little Pig not very big;
When he was alive he liv'd in clover,
  But now he is dead and that's all over;
Johnny Winckle, he sat down and cry'd,
  Betty Winckle, she laid down and dy'd;
So there was an end of one, two and three,
Johnny Winckle, He, Betty Winckle, She and Piggie Wiggie.

TWEEDLE-DUM

Tweedle-dum and Tweedle-dee
　　Resolved to have a battle,
For Tweedle-dum said Tweedle-dee
　　Had spoiled his nice new rattle.
Just then flew by a monstrous crow,
　　As big as a tar-barrel,
Which frightened both the heroes so,
　　They quite forgot their quarrel.

MARY'S LAMB

Mary had a little lamb,
  Its fleece was white as snow;
And everywhere that Mary went
  The lamb was sure to go.

It followed her to school one day:
  Which was against the rule;
It made the children laugh and play
  To see a lamb at school.

And so the teacher turned it out,
  But still it lingered near,
And waited patiently about
  Till Mary did appear.

"What makes the lamb love
    Mary so?"
The eager children cry.
"Why, Mary loves the lamb,
    you know,"
The teacher did reply.

DING, DONG, BELL

Ding, dong, bell,
Pussy's in the well!
Who put her in?—
Little Johnny Green.
Who pulled her out?—
Big Johnny Stout.
What a naughty boy was that
To drown poor pussy cat,
Who never did him any harm,
But killed the mice in his father's
    barn!

THREE CHILDREN
SLIDING ON THE ICE

Three children sliding on the ice
    Upon a summer's day;
As it fell out, they all fell in,
    The rest they ran away.

Now had these children been
    at home,
    Or sliding on dry ground,
Ten thousand pounds to
    one penny
    They had not all been drowned.

LITTLE TOMMY
TITTLEMOUSE

Little Tommy Tittlemouse
Lived in a little house;
He caught fishes
In other men's ditches.

SIMPLE SIMON

Simple Simon met a pieman,
    Going to the fair;
Says Simple Simon to the pieman,
    "Let me taste your ware."

Says the pieman to Simple Simon,
    "Show me first your penny."
Says Simple Simon to the pieman,
    "Indeed I have not any."

He went to catch a dickey-bird,
    And thought he could not fail,
Because he'd got a little salt
    To put upon his tail.

He went to shoot a wild duck,
    But wild duck flew away;
Says Simon, "I can't hit him,
    Because he will not stay."

Simple Simon went a-fishing
　　For to catch a whale;
All the water he had got
　　Was in his mother's pail.

He went to ride a spotted cow,
　　That had a little calf,
She threw him down upon the ground,
　　Which made the people laugh.

Simple Simon went to look
　　If plums grew on a thistle;
He pricked his fingers very much,
　　Which made poor Simon whistle.

He went for water in a sieve,
　　But soon it all ran through;
And now poor Simple Simon
　　Bids you all adieu.

DEEDLE, DEEDLE DUMPLING

Deedle, deedle dumpling, my son John,
He went to bed with his stockings on;
One stocking off, and one stocking on,
Deedle, deedle dumpling, my son John.

WHAT ARE LITTLE BOYS MADE OF?

What are little boys made of, made of?
What are little boys made of?
Frogs and snails, and puppy-dogs' tails;
And that's what little boys are made of, made of.

What are little girls made of, made of?
What are little girls made of?
Sugar and spice, and all that's nice;
And that's what little girls are made of, made of.

16

I LOVE LITTLE PUSSY

I love little pussy, her coat is so warm,
And if I don't hurt her, she'll do me no harm;
I'll not pull her tail, nor drive her away,
But pussy and I very gently will play.

TAFFY WAS A WELSHMAN

Taffy was a Welshman, Taffy was a thief;
Taffy came to my house and stole a piece of beef.

I went to Taffy's house, Taffy was not home;
Taffy came to my house and stole a marrow-bone.

I went to Taffy's house, Taffy was in bed,
I took the marrow-bone and beat him on the head.

17

CUSHY COW

Cushy cow bonny, let down thy milk,
And I will give thee a gown of silk;
A gown of silk and a silver tee
If thou wilt let down thy milk to me.

LITTLE POLLY FLINDERS

Little Polly Flinders
Sat among the cinders,
　Warming her pretty little toes!
Her mother came and caught her,
And whipped her little daughter
　For spoiling her nice new
　　clothes.

WEE WILLIE WINKIE

Wee Willie Winkie runs through
　the town,
Up-stairs and down-stairs, in his
　night-gown;
Rapping at the window, crying
　at the lock,
"Are the babes in their beds,
　for now it's eight o'clock."

SEE, SAW, MARGERY DAW

See, saw, Margery Daw,
Sold her bed and lay upon straw;
Was not she a dirty slut,
To sell her bed and lie in the dirt?

CHARLEY LOVES GOOD CAKES

Charley loves good cakes and ale,
　Charley loves good candy,
Charley loves to kiss the girls
　When they are clean and handy.

PEASE-PORRIDGE HOT

Pease-porridge hot,
　Pease-porridge cold,
Pease-porridge in the pot,
　Nine days old.

WHEN YOU'RE CALLED

Come when you're called,
  Do what you're bid,
Shut the door after you,
  Never be chid.

CURLY LOCKS

Curly locks! curly locks! wilt thou
    be mine?
Thou shalt not wash dishes,
    nor yet feed the swine,
But sit on a cushion and sew
    a fine seam,
And feed upon strawberries,
    sugar, and cream!

MATTHEW, MARK . . .

Matthew, Mark, Luke and John
Guard the bed that I lie on!
Four corners to my bed,
Four angels round my head;
One to watch, one to pray,
And two to bear my soul away.

LADY BIRD, LADY BIRD

Lady bird, lady bird, fly away
    home,
Thy house is on fire, thy
    children all gone,
All but one, and her name is Ann,
And she crept under the
    pudding-pan.

GEORGIE PORGIE

Georgie Porgie, pudding and pie,
Kissed the girls and made them cry.
When the boys came out to play
Georgie Porgie ran away.

TELL TALE, TIT!

Tell tale, tit!
Your tongue shall be slit,
And all the dogs in our town
Shall have a little bit.

THE HOUSE THAT JACK BUILT

THIS is the HOUSE that Jack built

This is the MALT
That lay in the house that Jack built.

This is the RAT that ate the malt,
That lay in the house that Jack built.

This is the CAT,
That killed the rat, that ate the malt,
That lay in the house that Jack built.

This is the DOG,
That worried the cat,
That killed the rat, that ate the malt,
That lay in the house that Jack built.

This is the COW with the crumpled horn,
That tossed the dog, that worried the cat,
That killed the rat, that ate the malt,
That lay in the house that Jack built.

This is the MAIDEN all forlorn,
That milked the cow with the crumpled horn,
That tossed the dog, . . . that worried the cat,
That killed the rat, . . . that ate the malt,
That lay in the house that Jack built.

This is the MAN all tattered and torn,
That kissed the maiden all forlorn,
That milked the cow with the crumpled horn,
That tossed the dog, . . . that worried the cat,
That killed the rat, . . . that ate the malt,
That lay in the house that Jack built.

This is the PRIEST all shaven and shorn,
That married the man all tattered and torn,
That kissed the maiden all forlorn,
That milked the cow with the crumpled horn,
That tossed the dog, . . . that worried the cat,
That killed the rat, . . . that ate the malt,
That lay in the house that Jack built.

This is the COCK that crowed in the morn,
That waked the priest all shaven and shorn,
That married the man all tattered and torn,
That kissed the maiden all forlorn,
That milked the cow with the crumpled horn,
That tossed the dog, . . . that worried the cat,
That killed the rat, . . . that ate the malt,
That lay in the house that Jack built.

This is the FARMER that sowed the corn,
That kept the cock that crowed in the morn,
That waked the priest all shaven and shorn,
That married the man all tattered and torn,
That kissed the maiden all forlorn,
That milked the cow with the crumpled horn,
That tossed the dog, that worried the cat,
That killed the rat, that ate the malt,
That lay in the house that Jack built.

23

OLD MOTHER GOOSE

Old Mother Goose
   When she wanted to wander,
Would ride through the air
   On a very fine gander.

Mother Goose had a house,
   'Twas built in a wood,
An owl at the door
   For a porter stood.

She sent him to market,
   A live goose he bought;
"Here! mother," says he,
   "It will not go for nought."

Jack's goose and her gander
   Grew very fond;
They'd both eat together,
   Or swim in one pond.

She had a son Jack,
   A plain-looking lad,
He was not very good,
   Nor yet very bad.

Jack found one morning,
   As I have been told,
His goose had laid him
   An egg of pure gold.

Jack rode to his mother,
   The news for to tell.
She called him a good boy,
   And said it was well.

Jack sold his gold egg
    To a rascally knave.
Not half of its value
    To poor Jack he gave.

Then Jack went courting
    A lady so gay,
As fair as a lily,
    And sweet as the May.

The knave and the squire
    Came up at his back,
And began to belabor
    The sides of poor Jack.

But Old Mother Goose
    That instant came in,
And turned her son Jack
    Into famed Harlequin.

She then with her wand
    Touched the lady so fine,
And turned her at once
    Into sweet Columbine.

The gold egg in the sea
    Was thrown away then—
When Jack he jumped in
    And got it again.

And Old Mother Goose
    The goose saddled soon,
And, mounting his back,
    Flew up to the moon.

AS TOMMY SNOOKS AND BESSY BROOKS

As Tommy Snooks and Bessy Brooks
Were walking out one Sunday,
Says Tommy Snooks to Bessy Brooks,
Wilt marry me on Monday?
Tomorrow will be Monday.

WHEN I WAS A BACHELOR

When I was a bachelor I lived by myself,
And all the meat I got I put upon a shelf.
The rats and the mice did lead me such a life,
That I went to London, to get myself a wife.

   The streets were so broad, and the lanes were so narrow,
   I could not get my wife home without a wheelbarrow,
   The wheelbarrow broke, my wife got a fall,
   Down tumbled wheelbarrow, little wife, and all.

TO MARKET, TO MARKET, TO BUY A PLUM BUN

To market, to market, to buy a plum bun;
Home again, home again, market is done.

FA, FE, FI, FO, FUM!

Fa, Fe, Fi, Fo, Fum!
I smell the blood of an Englishman:
Be he alive or be he dead,
I'll grind his bones to make me bread.

DOCTOR FAUSTUS WAS A GOOD MAN

Doctor Faustus was a good man,
He whipped his scholars now and then;
When he whipped them, he made them dance
Out of Scotland into France,
Out of France into Spain,
And then he whipped them back again!

DINGTY, DIDDLETY

Dingty, diddlety, my mammy's maid,
She stole oranges, I am afraid;
Some in her pocket, some in her sleeve,
She stole oranges, I do believe.

THE ROSE IS RED

The rose is red, the violet blue,
  The gilly flower sweet,—and so are you.
These are the words you bade me say
  For a pair of new gloves on Easter-day.

RIDE A COCK-HORSE

Ride a cock-horse to Banbury Cross,
  To buy little Johnny a galloping horse.
He trots behind and it ambles before,
  And Johnny shall ride until he can ride no more.

COME, BUTTER, COME

Come, butter, come,
Come, butter, come!
Peter stands at the gate,
Waiting for a buttered cake;
Come, butter, come!

BLESS
YOU, BURNIE BEE

Bless you, bless you, burnie bee;
Say, when will your wedding be?
If it be to-morrow day,
Take your wings and fly away.

NOSE, NOSE, JOLLY RED
NOSE

Nose, nose, jolly red nose,
And what gave you that jolly
        red nose?
Nutmegs and cinnamon, spices
        and cloves,
And they gave me this jolly
        red nose.

MISTRESS MARY

Mistress Mary, quite contrary,
    How does your garden grow?
With cockle shells, and silver bells,
    And pretty maids
        all in a row.

I WON'T BE MY FATHER'S
JACK

I won't be my father's Jack,
    I won't be my mother's Jill,
I will be the fiddler's wife,
    And have music when I will.
        T'other little tune,
        T'other little tune,
        Pr'ythee, love, play me
        T'other little tune.

30

THERE WAS A LITTLE BOY

There was a little boy and there was
   a little girl,
   Liv'd in an alley;
Says the little boy to the little girl,
   "Shall I, oh shall I?"

Says the little girl to the little boy,
   "What shall we do?"
Says the little boy to the little girl,
   "I will kiss you."

THERE WAS A JOLLY MILLER

There was a jolly miller
Lived on the river Dee,
He looked upon his pillow,
And there he saw a flea.
"O! Mr. Flea,
You have been biting me,
And you must die:"
So he cracked his bones
Upon the stones,
And there he let him die.

JACK AND JILL

Jack and Jill went up the hill
   To fetch a pail of water,
Jack fell down and broke his crown
   And Jill came tumbling after.

Up Jack got, and home did trot
   As fast as he could caper.
Went to bed and bound his head
   With vinegar and brown paper.

A COUNT FOR GAMES

Intery, mintery, cutery-corn,
Apple seed and apple thorn;
Wire brier limber-lock,
Five geese in a flock,
Sit and sing by a spring,
O-u-t, and in again.

DOCTOR FOSTER

Doctor Foster went to Gloucester,
    In a shower of rain;
He stepped in a puddle up to his middle,
    And never went there again.

THE SOW CAME IN

The sow came in with the saddle,
The little pig rocked the cradle,
The dish jumped over the table
To see the pot wash the ladle.
The spit that stood behind the door
Called dish-clout dirty, o'er and o'er.
"What!" said the gridiron, "can't you agree?
I am the head constable, come along with me."

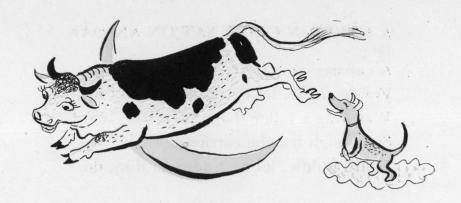

HEY, DIDDLE, DIDDLE

Hey, diddle, diddle, the cat and the fiddle,
    The cow jumped over the moon;
The little dog laughed to see such sport,
    And the dish ran away with the spoon.

ONE MISTY, MOISTY MORNING

One misty, moisty morning,
    When cloudy was the weather,
I chanced to meet an old man
    Clothed all in leather;
He began to compliment,
    And I began to grin,—
"How do you do," and "How do you do,"
    And "How do you do" again!

A CARRION CROW SAT ON AN OAK

A carrion crow sat on an oak,
Fol de riddle, lol de riddle, hi ding do,
Watching a tailor shape his cloak;
Sing heigh ho, the carrion crow,
Fol de riddle, lol de riddle, hi ding do.

Wife, bring me my old bent bow,
Fol de riddle, lol de riddle, hi ding do,
That I may shoot yon carrion crow;
Sing heigh ho, the carrion crow,
Fol de riddle, lol de riddle, hi ding do.

The tailor he shot, and missed his mark,
Fol de riddle, lol de riddle, hi ding do,
And shot his own sow quite through the heart;
Sing heigh ho, the carrion crow,
Fol de riddle, lol de riddle, hi ding do.

Wife, bring brandy in a spoon,
Fol de riddle, lol de riddle, hi ding do,
For our old sow is in a swoon;
Sing heigh ho, the carrion crow,
Fol de riddle, lol de riddle, hi ding do.

COCK A DOODLE DOO!

Cock a doodle doo!
My dame has lost her shoe;
My master's lost his fiddling-stick,
And don't know what to do.

Cock a doodle doo!
What is my dame to do?
Till master finds his fiddling-stick,
She'll dance without her shoe.

594544

Cock a doodle doo!
My dame has lost her shoe,
And master's found his fiddling-stick,
Sing doodle doodle doo!

Cock a doodle doo!
My dame will dance with you,
While master fiddles his fiddling-stick,
For dame and doodle doo.

Cock a doodle doo!
Dame has lost her shoe;
Gone to bed and scratched her head,
And can't tell what to do.

MY LADY WIND

Lady Wind, my Lady Wind,
Went round about the house, to find
  A chink to get her foot in;
She tried the keyhole in the door,
She tried the crevice in the floor,
  And drove the chimney soot in.

And then one night, when it was dark,
She blew up such a tiny spark,
  That all the house was pothered;
From it she raised up such a flame,
As flamed away to Belting Lane,
  And White Cross folks were smothered.

And thus when once, my little dears,
A whisper reaches itching ears,
  The same will come, you'll find;
Take my advice, restrain the tongue,
Remember what old nurse has sung
  Of busy Lady Wind.

THE BABES IN THE WOOD

My dear, do you know
How a long time ago
Two poor little children,
Whose names I don't know,
Were stolen away on a fine summer's day,
And left in a wood, as I've heard people say.

And when it was night,
So sad was their plight,
The sun it went down,
And the moon gave no light!
They sobbed, and they sighed, and they bitterly cried,
And the poor little things, they lay down and died.

And when they were dead,
The Robins so red
Brought strawberry leaves,
And over them spread;
And all the day long,
They sung them this song:
"Poor babes in the wood! poor babes in the wood!
And don't you remember the babes in the wood?"

LITTLE BETTY BLUE

Little Betty Blue
　　Lost her holiday shoe.
What shall little Betty do?
　　Buy her another
To match the other,
　　And then she'll walk in two.

I HAD A LITTLE PONY

I had a little pony,
His name was Dapple-gray;
I lent him to a lady
To ride a mile away;
She whipped him, she slashed him,
She rode him through the mire;
I would not lend my pony now
For all the lady's hire.

MARGERY MUTTON-PIE

Margery Mutton-pie
　　and Johnny Bopeep,
They met together
　　in Grace-church street;
In and out, in and out,
　　over the way,
O! says Johnny, 'tis
　　chop-a-nose day.

LAVENDER'S BLUE

Lavender's blue, dilly dilly,
　　lavender's green;
When I am king, dilly dilly,
　　you shall be queen;
Call up your men, dilly dilly,
　　set them to work;
Some to the plough, dilly-dilly,
　　some to the cart;
Some to make hay, dilly dilly,
　　some to cut corn;
While you and I, dilly dilly,
　　keep ourselves warm.

POLLY, PUT THE KETTLE ON

Polly, put the kettle on,
Polly, put the kettle on,
Polly, put the kettle on,
   And let's drink tea.

Sukey, take it off again,
Sukey, take it off again,
Sukey, take it off again,
   They're all gone away.

DAFFY-DOWN-DILLY

Daffy-down-dilly has come
   up to town,
In a yellow petticoat and a
   green gown.

LITTLE JUMPING JOAN

Here am I, little Jumping Joan,
When nobody's with me,
   I'm always alone.

LITTLE TOMMY TUCKER

Little Tommy Tucker
   Sings for his supper.
What shall he eat?
   White bread and butter.

How shall he cut it
   Without e'er a knife?
How shall he marry
   Without any wife?

LITTLE MISS MUFFET

Little Miss Muffet
Sat on a tuffet,
Eating her curds and whey.
There came a great spider,
And sat down beside her,
And frightened Miss Muffet away!

A FARMER WENT TROTTING

A farmer went trotting upon his grey mare,
    Bumpety, bumpety, bump!
With his daughter behind him, so rosy and fair,
    Lumpety, lumpety, lump!

A raven cried croak! and they all tumbled down,
    Bumpety, bumpety, bump!
The mare broke her knees, and the farmer his crown,
    Lumpety, lumpety, lump!

The mischievous raven flew laughing away,
    Bumpety, bumpety, bump!
And vowed he would serve them the same the next day,
    Lumpety, lumpety, lump!

GIRLS AND BOYS, COME OUT TO PLAY

Girls and boys, come out to play,
The moon doth shine as bright as day;
Leave your supper and leave your sleep,
And come with your playfellows into the street.
Come with a whoop, come with a call,
Come with a good will or not at all,
Up the ladder and down the wall,
A half-penny roll will serve us all.
You find milk, and I'll find flour,
And we'll have a pudding in half an hour.

41

THE MAN IN THE WILDERNESS

The man in **the** wilderness asked me,
How many strawberries grew in the sea.
I answered him, as I thought good,
As many red herrings as grew in the wood.

THERE WAS AN OLD WOMAN WHO LIVED IN A SHOE

There was an old woman who lived in a shoe,
She had so many children she didn't know what to do;
She gave them some broth, without any bread,
She whipped them all soundly and sent them to bed.

KING PIPPIN'S HALL

King Pippin he built a fine new hall,
Pastry and piecrust that was the wall;
The windows were made of black pudding and white,
Slated with pancakes,—you ne'er saw the like.

AS I WAS GOING TO SELL MY EGGS

As I was going to sell my eggs,
I met a man with bandy legs,
Bandy legs and crooked toes,
I tripped up his heels and he fell on his nose.

I HAD A LITTLE MOPPET

I had a little moppet,
I put it in my pocket,
    And fed it with corn and hay;
Then came a proud beggar,
And swore he would have her,
    And stole my moppet away.

FOR WANT OF A NAIL

For want of a nail the shoe was lost,
For want of the shoe, the horse was lost,
For want of the horse, the rider was lost,
For want of the rider, the battle was lost,
For want of the battle, the kingdom was lost,
And all for want of a horseshoe nail!

ROBERT BARNES

"Robert Barnes, fellow fine,
  Can you shoe this horse of mine?"
"Yes, good sir, that I can,
  As well as any other man:
  Here a nail, and there a prod,
  And now, good sir, your horse is shod."

HOW MANY MILES TO BABYLON?

How many miles to Babylon?
  Threescore miles and ten.
Can I get there by candle-light?
  Yes, and back again!
If your heels are nimble and light,
You may get there by candle-light.

OLD KING COLE

Old King Cole was a merry old soul
   And a merry old soul was he;
He called for his pipe and he called for his glass
   And he called for his fiddlers three!

Every fiddler he had a fine fiddle,
   And a very fine fiddle had he;
Twee-tweedle-dee, tweedle-dee, went the fiddlers.
Oh, there's none so rare as can compare
   With King Cole and his fiddlers three!

Old King Cole was a merry old soul
   And a merry old soul was he;
He called for his pipe and he called for his glass
   And he called for his pipers three!

Every piper he had a fine pipe,
   And a very fine pipe had he;
Then tootle-tootle-too, tootle-too, went the pipers.
Oh, there's none so rare as can compare
   With King Cole and his pipers three!

GOOD KING ARTHUR

When good King Arthur ruled this land,
   He was a goodly King;
He bought three pecks of barley-meal,
   To make a bag-pudding.

A bag-pudding the King did make,
   And stuffed it well with plums,
And in it put great lumps of fat,
   As big as my two thumbs.

The King and Queen did eat thereof,
   And noblemen beside;
And what they could not eat that night,
   The Queen next morning fried.

THERE WAS AN OLD WOMAN SAT SPINNING

There was an old woman sat
　　spinning,
And that's the beginning.
She had a calf
And that's half;
She took it by the tail,
And threw it over the wall,
And that's all.

HARK, HARK

Hark, hark,
The dogs do bark,
The beggars are coming to town;
Some in rags,
Some in bags,
And some in velvet gowns.

TO BED, TO BED

"To bed, to bed," says Sleepy-head.
"Tarry a while," says Slow;
"Put on the pan," says Greedy Nan,
"We'll sup before we go."

BOW, WOW, WOW

Bow, wow, wow,
Whose dog art thou?
Little Tom Tinker's dog,
Bow, wow, wow.

THE QUEEN OF HEARTS

The queen of hearts,
She made some tarts,
All on a summer's day;
The knave of hearts,
He stole those tarts,
And with them ran away:
The king of hearts
Called for those tarts,
And beat the knave full sore;
The knave of hearts
Brought back those tarts,
And said he'd ne'er steal more.

SOLOMON GRUNDY

Solomon Grundy,
Born on a Monday,
Christened on Tuesday,
Married on Wednesday,
Took ill on Thursday,
Worse on Friday,
Died on Saturday,
Buried on Sunday:
This is the end
Of Solomon Grundy.

THE MAN
IN THE MOON

The man in the moon
Came down too soon,
To inquire his way to Norwich.
He went by the south,
And burnt his mouth
With eating cold plum-porridge.

WE'RE
ALL IN THE DUMPS

We're all in the dumps,
For diamonds are trumps,
The kittens are gone to St. Paul's!
The babies are bit,
The moon's in a fit,
And the houses are built without
walls.

AS I WAS GOING UP
PIPPEN HILL

As I was going up Pippen Hill—
Pippen Hill was dirty—
There I met a pretty miss,
And she dropped me a curtsey.

Little miss, pretty miss,
Blessings light upon you!
If I had half-a-crown a day,
I'd spend it all upon you.

49

LITTLE BO-PEEP

Little Bo-Peep has lost her sheep,
   And can't tell where to find them;
Leave them alone, and they'll come home
And bring their tails behind them.

Little Bo-Peep fell fast asleep,
   And dreamt she heard them bleating;
But when she awoke she found it a joke,
   For still they all were fleeting.

Then up she took her little crook,
   Determined for to find them;
She found them indeed, but it made her heart bleed,
   For they'd left their tails behind them.

It happened one day, as Bo-Peep did stray
    Unto a meadow hard by,
There she espied their tails, side by side,
    All hung on a tree to dry.

She heaved a sigh, and wiped her eye,
    And ran o'er hill and dale,
And tried what she could, as a shepherdess should,
    To tack to each sheep its tail.

IF I'D AS MUCH MONEY AS I COULD SPEND

If I'd as much money as I could spend,
I never would cry old chairs to mend;
Old chairs to mend, old chairs to mend;
I never would cry old chairs to mend.

If I'd as much money as I could tell,
I never would cry old clothes to sell;
Old clothes to sell, old clothes to sell;
I never would cry old clothes to sell.

THERE WAS AN OLD WOMAN

There was an old woman tossed up in a basket,
   Seventeen times as high as the moon;
And where she was going, I couldn't but ask it,
   For in her hand she carried a broom.

"Old woman, old woman, old woman," said I,
   "O whither, O whither, O whither so high?"
"To sweep the cobwebs off the sky!"
   "Shall I go with you?" "Aye, by-and-by."

BRYAN O'LYNN

Bryan O'Lynn and his wife and wife's mother
They all went over the bridge together;
The bridge was broken; they all fell in;
The deuce go with all! quoth Bryan O'Lynn.

JACK SPRAT

Jack Sprat could eat no fat,
His wife could eat no lean;
And so betwixt them both, you see,
They licked the platter clean.

LITTLE JACK HORNER

Little Jack Horner sat in a corner,
Eating a Christmas pie;
He put in his thumb, and took out a plum,
And said, "What a good boy am I!"

OLD WOMAN, OLD WOMAN, SHALL WE GO A-SHEARING?

Old woman, old woman, shall we go a-shearing?
"Speak a little louder, sir, I am very thick of hearing."
Old woman, old woman, shall I love you dearly?
"Thank you, kind sir, I hear you very clearly.'

JOHN COOK HE HAD A LITTLE GRAY MARE

John Cook he had a little gray mare;
  Hee, haw, hum!
Her back stood up and her bones were bare;
  Hee, haw, hum!

John Cook was riding up Shooter's bank;
  Hee, haw, hum!
The mare she began to kick and to prank;
  Hee, haw, hum!

John Cook was riding up Shooter's hill;
  Hee, haw, hum!
His mare fell down, and made her will;
  Hee, haw, hum!

The bridle and saddle were laid on the shelf;
  Hee, haw, hum!
If you want any more you may sing it yourself;
  Hee, haw, hum!

I LOVE SIXPENCE

I love sixpence, pretty little sixpence,
  I love sixpence better than my life;
I spent a penny of it, I spent another,
  And took fourpence home to my wife.

Oh, my little fourpence, pretty little fourpence,
  I love fourpence better than my life;
I spent a penny of it, I spent another,
  And took twopence home to my wife.

Oh, my little twopence, my pretty little twopence,
  I love twopence better than my life;
I spent a penny of it, I spent another,
  And I took nothing home to my wife.

Oh, my little nothing, my pretty little nothing,
  What will nothing buy for my wife?
I have nothing, I spend nothing,
  I love nothing better than my wife.

BARBER, SHAVE A PIG

Barber, barber, shave a pig,
How many hairs will make a wig?
"Four and twenty, that's enough."
Give the poor barber a pinch of snuff.

PETER, PETER, PUMPKIN-EATER

Peter, Peter, pumpkin-eater,
Had a wife and couldn't keep her;
He put her in a pumpkin shell,
And there he kept her very well.

TOMMY TROT, A MAN OF LAW

Tommy Trot, a man of law,
Sold his bed and lay upon straw;
Sold the straw and slept on grass,
To buy his wife a looking-glass.

THREE WISE MEN OF GOTHAM

Three wise men of Gotham
Went to sea in a bowl;
If the bowl had been stronger
My song had been longer.

ONE TO TEN

1, 2, 3, 4, 5,
I caught a hare alive;
6, 7, 8, 9, 10,
I let her go again.

PAT-A-CAKE

Pat-a-cake, pat-a-cake, baker's man!
So I will, master, as fast as I can:
Pat it, and prick it, and mark it with T,
Put it in the oven for [*Tommy*] and me.

A, B, C, TUMBLE DOWN D

A, B, C, tumble down D,
The cat's in the cupboard, and can't see me.

ONE, TWO, BUCKLE MY SHOE

1-2
One, two,
Buckle my shoe;

3-4
Three, four,
Shut the door;

5-6
Five, six,
Pick up sticks;

7-8
Seven, eight,
Lay them straight;

9-10
Nine, ten,
A good fat hen;

11-12
Eleven, twelve,
Who will delve?

13-14
Thirteen, fourteen,
Maids a-courting;

15-16
Fifteen, sixteen,
Maids in the kitchen;

17-18
Seventeen, eighteen,
Maids in waiting;

19-20
Nineteen, twenty,
My stomach's empty.

A was an apple-tart;

B bit it;

E eat it;

F fought for it;

J joined it;

K kept it;

N nodded at it;

O opened it;

R ran for it;

S stole it;

W wanted it;

X,

C cut it;

D dealt it;

G got it;

H had it;

L longed for it;

M mourned for it;

P peeped in it;

Q quartered it;

T took it;

V viewed it;

Y and

Z all wished a piece of it.

DANCE, THUMBKIN, DANCE

Dance, Thumbkin, dance,
    (Keep the thumb in motion.)

Dance, ye merry men, every one:
    (All the fingers in motion.)

For Thumbkin he can dance alone,
Thumbkin he can dance alone,
    (The thumb only moving.)

Dance, Foreman, dance,
    (The first finger moving.)

Dance, ye merry men, every one:
    (The whole moving.)

But Foreman he can dance alone,
Foreman he can dance alone.
    (The first finger only moving.)

Dance, Longman, dance,
    (The second finger only moving.)

Dance, ye merry men, every one:
    (The whole moving.)

But Longman he can dance alone,
Longman he can dance alone.
(And so on with the others, naming the third finger Ringman, the fourth Littleman. Littleman cannot dance alone.)

DANCE A BABY DIDDIT

Dance a baby diddit,
What can his mother do with it,
But sit in a lap,
And give him some pap?
Dance a baby diddit.

HUSH-A-BYE, BABY

Hush-a-bye, baby,
    Daddy is near;
Mamma is a lady,
    And that's very clear.

THIS IS THE WAY
THE LADIES RIDE

This is the way the ladies ride:
Trot, trot, trot!
This is the way the gentlemen ride:
Gallop-a-trot! Gallop-a-trot!
This is the way the farmers ride:
Hobbledy-hoy! Hobbledy-hoy!

THIS LITTLE PIG

This little Pig went to Market,
This little Pig stayed at Home,
This little Pig had Roast Beef,
This little Pig had none,
This little Pig cried wee, wee, wee,
All the way home.

SHOE THE COLT

Shoe the colt,
Shoe the colt,
Shoe the wild mare;
Here a nail,
There a nail,
Yet she goes bare.

DANCE TO YOUR DADDY

Dance to your daddy,
My little babby;
Dance to your daddy,
My little lamb.
You shall have a fishy,
In a little dishy;
You shall have a fishy,
When the boat comes in.

JACK BE NIMBLE

Jack be nimble,
Jack be quick,
Jack jump over the
candlestick.

BYE, BABY BUNTING

Bye, baby bunting,
Daddy's gone a hunting,
To get a little rabbit's skin
To wrap the baby bunting in.

ROCK-A-BYE, BABY

Rock-a-bye, baby, the cradle is green;
Father's a nobleman, mother's a queen;
Betty's a lady, and wears a gold ring;
Johnny's a drummer and drums for the king.

HUSH-A-BYE, BABY, ON THE TREE-TOP

Hush-a-bye, baby, on the tree-top,
When the wind blows, the cradle will rock;
When the bough bends, the cradle will fall,
Down will come baby, bough, cradle, and all.

HERE GOES MY LORD

Here goes my lord
A trot, a trot, a trot, a trot,
Here goes my lady
A canter, a canter, a canter, a canter!
Here goes my young master
Jockey-hitch, Jockey-hitch, Jockey-hitch, Jockey-hitch;
Here goes my young miss,
An amble, an amble, an amble, an amble!
The footman lags behind to tipple ale and wine,
And goes gallop, a gallop, a gallop, a gallop, to make up his time.

HANDY SPANDY

Handy Spandy, Jack-a-dandy,
Loved plum cake and sugar candy;
He bought some at a grocer's shop,
And out he came, hop, hop, hop.

HERE SITS THE LORD MAYOR

Here sits the Lord Mayor, [*forehead*]
   Here sit his two men; [*eyes*]
Here sits the cock, [*right cheek*]
   Here sits the hen; [*left cheek*]

Here sit the little chickens [*tip of nose*]
   Here they run in; [*mouth*]
Chinchopper, chinchopper,
   Chinchopper, chin! [*chuck the chin*]

HEY, MY KITTEN, MY KITTEN

Hey, my kitten, my kitten,
   And hey, my kitten, my deary!
Such a sweet pet as this
   Was neither far nor neary.

Here we go up, up, up,
   And here we go down, down, downy,
And here we go backwards and forwards,
   And here we go round, round, roundy.

67

RIDDLES

As soft as silk, as white as milk,
As bitter as gall, a thick wall,
And a rough coat covers me all. [A WALNUT]

As round as an apple, as deep as a cup,
And all the king's horses can't pull it up. [A WELL]

Two legs sat upon three legs,
With one leg in his lap;
In comes four legs,
And runs away with one leg.
Up jumps two legs,
Catches up three legs,
Throws it after four legs,
And makes him bring back one leg.

[One Leg: A LEG OF MUTTON
Two Legs: A MAN
Three Legs: A STOOL
Four Legs: A DOG]

As I was going o'er London Bridge,
I met a cart full of fingers and thumbs! [GLOVES]

Little Nanny Etticoat,
In a white petticoat
And a red nose;
The longer she stands,
The shorter she grows. [A CANDLE]

Old Mother Twitchett had but one eye,
And a long tail which she let fly;
And every time she went through a gap,
A bit of her tail she left in a trap. [A NEEDLE]

Humpty-Dumpty sat on a wall,
Humpty-Dumpty had a great fall;
All the King's horses, and all the King's men,
Couldn't put Humpty-Dumpty together again. [AN EGG]

I have a little sister, they call her peep, peep;
She wades the waters deep, deep, deep;
She climbs the mountains high, high, high;
Poor little creature, she has but one eye. [A STAR]

ADAGES

Birds of a feather flock together,
And so will pigs and swine;
Rats and mice will have their choice,
And so will I have mine.

If ifs and ands
Were pots and pans,
There would be no need for tinkers!

The Cock doth crow
To let you know:
If you be wise
'Tis time to rise.

Awake, arise, pull out your eyes,
And hear what time of day;
And when you have done, pull out
your tongue,
And see what you can say.

For every evil under the sun
There is a cure, or there is none.
If there be one, try and find it;
If there be none, never mind it.

Nature requires five,
   Custom gives seven!
Laziness takes nine,
   And wickedness eleven.

See a pin and pick it up,
All the day you'll have good luck;
See a pin and let it lie,
You'll wish you'd never passed it by!

He that would thrive
Must rise at five;
He that hath thriven
May lie till seven;
And he that by the plough would thrive
Himself must either hold or drive.

TONGUE TWISTERS

I would if I could,
If I couldn't, how could I?
I couldn't without I could, could I?
Could you, without you could, could ye?
Could ye, could ye?
Could you, without you could, could ye?

One old Oxford ox opening oysters;
Two tee-totums totally tired of trying to trot to Tadbury;
Three tall tigers tippling tenpenny tea;
Four fat friars fanning fainting flies;
Five frippy Frenchmen foolishly fishing for flies;
Six sportsmen shooting snipes;
Seven Severn salmons swallowing shrimps;
Eight Englishmen eagerly examining Europe;
Nine nimble noblemen nibbling nonpareils;
Ten tinkers tinkling upon ten tin tinder-boxes with tenpenny tacks;
Eleven elephants elegantly equipped;
Twelve typographical typographers typically translating types.

Three crooked cripples went through Cripplegate,
And through Cripplegate went three crooked cripples.

When a twister a-twisting, will twist him a twist,
For the twisting his twist, he three times doth intwist;
But if one of the twines of the twist do untwist,
The twine that untwisteth, untwisteth the twist.

Untwirling the twine that untwisteth between,
He twists, with the twister, the two in a twine;
Then twice having twisted the twines of the twine,
He twisteth the twine he had twined in twain.

The twain that, in twining, before in the twine,
As twines were intwisted, he now doth untwine;
'Twixt the twain intertwisting a twine more between,
He, twirling his twister, makes a twist of the twine.

THE WEATHER

Rain, rain, go away,
Come again another day;
Little Johnny wants to play.

When the days begin to lengthen,
The cold begins to strengthen.

When the wind is in the East,
'Tis neither good for man nor beast;
When the wind is in the North,
The skillful fisher goes not forth;
When the wind is in the South,
It blows the bait in the fishes' mouth;
When the wind is in the West,
Then 'tis at the very best.

A swarm of bees in May
Is worth a load of hay;
A swarm of bees in June
Is worth a silver spoon;
A swarm of bees in July
Is not worth a fly.

AND THE SEASONS

A sunshiny shower
Won't last half an hour.

Thirty days hath September,
April, June, and November;
All the rest have thirty-one
Except the second month alone
Which hath but twenty-eight in fine
Till leap-year makes it twenty-nine.

My learned friend and neighbor Pig,
Odds bobs and bells, and dash my wig;
'Tis said that you the weather know;
Please tell me when the wind will blow.

Cold and raw the north winds blow,
    Bleak in the morning early;
All the hills are covered with snow,
    And winter's now come fairly.

March winds and April showers
Bring forth May flowers.

AS I WAS GOING ALONG, LONG, LONG

As I was going along, long, long,
A-singing a comical song, song, song,
The lane that I went was so long, long, long,
And the song that I sung was as long, long, long,
And so I went singing along.

IF ALL THE WORLD WAS APPLE-PIE

If all the world was apple-pie,
    And all the sea was ink,
And all the trees were bread and cheese,
    What should we have for drink?

THERE WAS AN OLD WOMAN CALLED NOTHING-AT-ALL

There was an old woman called Nothing-at-all,
Who rejoiced in a dwelling exceedingly small;
A man stretched his mouth to its utmost extent,
And down at one gulp house and old woman went.

LITTLE BOY BLUE

Little Boy Blue, come, blow your horn;
The sheep's in the meadow, the cow's in the corn.
Where's the boy that looks after the sheep?
He's under the haystack, fast asleep.
Will you wake him? No, not I!
For if I do, he's sure to cry.

PETER WHITE

Peter White will never go right,
And would you know the reason why?
He follows his nose wherever he goes,
And that stands all awry.

THERE WAS AN OLD WOMAN LIVED UNDER A HILL

There was an old woman
Lived under a hill,
And if she's not gone,
She lives there still.

MY FATHER HE DIED

My father he died, but I can't tell you how;
He left me six horses to follow the plow:
With my wing wang waddle ho!
Jack sing saddle oh,
Blowsey boys bubble oh;
Under the broom.

I sold my six horses to buy me a cow,
And wasn't that a pretty thing to follow the plow?
With my, &c.

I sold my cow to buy me a calf,
I'd fain have made my fortune, but lost the best half.
With my, &c.

I sold my calf to buy me a cat,
A pretty thing she was, in my chimney sat,
With my, &c.

I sold my cat to buy me a mouse,
He carried fire in his tail, and burnt down my house.
With my, &c.

A FROG HE WOULD A-WOOING GO

A Frog he would a-wooing go,
  Heigho, says Rowley:
Whether his mother would let him or no;
With a rowley powley, gammon and spinach,
Heigho, says Anthony Rowley.

So off he marched with his opera hat,
  Heigho, says Rowley,
And on the road he met with a rat.
With a rowley, etc.

"Pray, Mr. Rat, will you go with me?"
  Heigho, says Rowley,
"Kind Mrs. Mousey for to see?"
With a rowley, etc.

When they came to the door of Mousey's hall
    Heigho, says Rowley,
They gave a loud knock and they gave a loud call,
With a rowley, etc.

"Pray, Mrs. Mouse, are you within?"
    Heigho, says Rowley;
"Yes, kind sir, I am sitting to spin,"
    With a rowley, powley, etc.

"Pray, Mrs. Mouse, will you give us some beer?"
    Heigho, says Rowley;
"For Froggy and I are fond of good cheer,"
    With a rowley, powley, etc.

Now while they were all merry-making,
    Heigho, says Rowley,
The cat and her kittens came tumbling in,
    With a rowley, powley, etc.

80

The cat she seized the rat by the crown,
  Heigho, says Rowley,
The kittens they pulled the little mouse down,
  With a rowley, powley, etc.

This put Mr. Frog in a terrible fright,
  Heigho, says Rowley,
He took up his hat and he wished them good-night,
  With a rowley, powley, etc.

But as Froggy was crossing over a brook,
  Heigho, says Rowley,
A lily-white duck came and gobbled him up,
  With a rowley, powley, etc.

So there was an end of one, two, three,
  Heigho, says Rowley,
The Rat, the Mouse, and the little Frog-ee!
With a rowley, powley, gammon and spinach,
  Heigho, says Anthony Rowley.

A DOG AND A CAT

A dog and a cat went out together
To see some friends just out of town,
Said the cat to the dog:
"What d'ye think of the weather?"
"I think Ma'am, the rain will come down,
 But don't be alarmed, for I have an umbrella
 That will shelter us both," said this amiable fellow.

82

PUSSY SITS BY THE FIRE

Pussy sits by the fire,
   How did she come there?
In walks little doggy,
   Says, "Pussy, are you there?"
"How do you do, mistress Pussy?
   Mistress Pussy, how do you do?"
"I thank you kindly, little dog,
   I fare as well as you."

THE FOX AND HIS WIFE

The fox and his wife they had a great strife,
They never ate mustard in all their whole life;
They ate their meat without fork or knife,
    And loved to be picking a bone, e-ho!

The fox jumped up on a moonlight night;
The stars they were shining, and all things bright,
"O ho!" said the fox, "it's a very fine night
    For me to go through the town, e-ho!"

The fox when he came to yonder stile,
He lifted his lugs and he listened a while!
"O ho!" said the fox, "it's but a short mile
    From this unto yonder wee town, e-ho!"

The fox, when he came to the farmer's gate,
Who should he see but the farmer's drake;
"I love you well for your master's sake,
    And long to be picking your bone, e-ho!"

The gray goose she ran round the hay-stack,
"O ho!" said the fox, "you are very fat;
You'll grease my beard, and ride on my back
    From this unto yonder wee town, e-ho!"

Old Gammer Hipple-hopple hopped out of bed,
She opened the casement, and popped out her head:
"O husband! O husband! the gray goose is dead,
    And the fox has gone through the town, O!"

Then the old man got up in his red cap,
And swore he would catch the fox in a trap;
But the fox was too cunning, and gave him the slip,
    And ran through the town, the town, O!

When he got to the top of the hill,
He blew his trumpet both loud and shrill,
For joy that he was safe
    Through the town, O!

When the fox came back to his den,
He had young ones both nine and ten:
"You're welcome home, daddy, you may go again,
If you bring us such nice meat
    From the town, O!"

I HAVE LA-A-A-YED

Hen—Cock, cock, I have la-a-a-yed.
Cock—Hen, hen, that's well sa-a-a-id.
Hen—Although I have to go bare-footed every da-a-ay.
Cock—Sell your eggs and buy shoes!
Sell your eggs and buy shoes!

PUSSY CAT, WHERE HAVE YOU BEEN?

Pussy cat, pussy cat, where have you been?
I've been to London to see the Queen.
Pussy cat, pussy cat, what did you there?
I frightened a little mouse under the chair.

LITTLE ROBIN REDBREAST

Little Robin Redbreast jump'd upon a wall,
Pussy cat jump'd after him, and almost got a fall;
Little Robin chirp'd and sang, and what did Pussy say?
Pussy said "Mew" and Robin jump'd away.

A CAT CAME FIDDLING

A cat came fiddling out of a barn
With a pair of bag-pipes under her arm;
She could sing nothing but Fiddle-de-dee,
The mouse has married the bumble-bee;
Pipe, cat—dance, mouse—
We'll have a wedding at our good house.

LEG OVER LEG

Leg over leg,
    As the dog went to Dover;
When he came to a stile,
    Jump he went over.

HICKORY, DICKORY, DOCK

Hickory, dickory, dock,
The mouse ran up the clock,
    The clock struck one,
    The mouse ran down;
Hickory, dickory, dock.

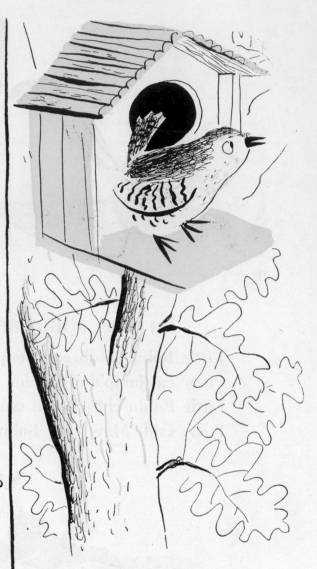

THE NORTH WIND

The north wind doth blow,
We soon shall have snow,
And what will poor Robin do then?
    Poor thing!

He'll sit in a barn,
To keep himself warm,
And hide his head under his wing:
    Poor thing!

HICKETY, PICKETY

Hickety, pickety, my black hen,
She lays eggs for gentlemen;
Gentlemen come every day
To see what my black hen doth lay.

LITTLE JENNY WREN

As little Jenny Wren
    Was sitting by the shed,
She waggled with her tail,
    And nodded with her head.

She waggled with her tail,
    And nodded with her head,
As little Jenny Wren
    Was sitting by the shed.

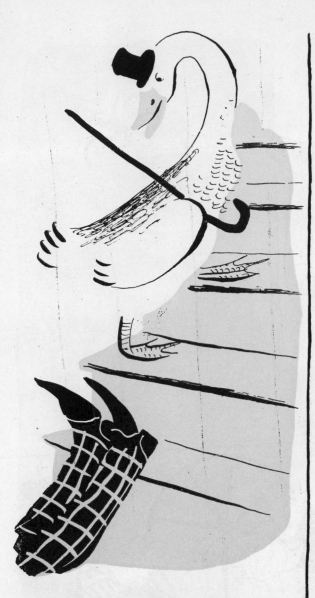

THERE WERE TWO BLACKBIRDS

There were two blackbirds,
  Sitting on a hill,
The one named Jack,
  The other named Jill;
Fly away, Jack!
  Fly away, Jill!
Come again, Jack!
  Come again, Jill!

A LONG-TAILED PIG

A long-tailed pig, or a short-tailed
  pig,
  Or a pig without e'er a tail,
A sow-pig, or a boar-pig,
  Or a pig with a curly tail.

DIDDLEDY, DIDDLEDY, DUMPTY

Diddledy, diddledy, dumpty;
The cat ran up the plum tree.
  I'll lay you a crown
  I'll fetch you down;
So diddledy, diddledy, dumpty.

PIT, PAT, WELL-A DAY!

Pit, pat, well-a day!
Little Robin flew away.
Where can little Robin be?
Up in yonder cherry-tree.

GOOSEY, GOOSEY, GANDER

Goosey, goosey, gander,
Where shall I wander?
Up stairs, down stairs,
And in my lady's chamber.

There I met an old man
That would not say his prayers.
I took him by the left leg,
And threw him down the stairs.

SOME LITTLE MICE

Some little mice sat in a barn to spin;
Pussy came by, and popped his head in;
"Shall I come in, and cut your threads off?"
"O! no, kind sir, you would snap our heads off."

90

A LITTLE PIG

A little pig found a fifty-dollar note
And purchased a hat and a very fine coat,
   With trousers and stockings and shoes;
Cravat, and shirt-collar, and gold-headed cane;
Then proud as could be, did he march up the lane,
   Says he, "I shall hear all the news."

THE STORY OF JENNY WREN AND COCK ROBIN

'Twas on a merry time, when Jenny Wren was young.
So neatly as she danced, and so sweetly as she sung,—

Robin Redbreast lost his heart—he was a gallant bird;
He doffed his hat to Jenny, and thus to her he said:—

"My dearest Jenny Wren, if you will but be mine,
You shall dine on cherry-pie, and drink nice currant-wine.

"I'll dress you like a Goldfinch, or like a Peacock gay;
So if you'll have me, Jenny, let us appoint the day."

Jenny blushed behind her fan, and thus declared her mind;
"Then let it be to-morrow, Bob; I take your offer kind.

"Cherry-pie is very good; so is currant-wine;
But I will wear my brown gown, and never dress too fine."

Robin rose up early, at the break of day;
He flew to Jenny Wren's house, to sing a roundelay.

He met the Cock and Hen, and bade the Cock declare,
This was his wedding-day with Jenny Wren the fair.

The Cock then blew his horn, to let the neighbors know
This was Robin's wedding-day, and they might see the show.

And first came Parson Rook, with his spectacles and band;
And one of Mother Goose's books he held within his hand.

Then followed him the Lark, for he could sweetly sing;
And he was to be clerk at Cock Robin's wedding.

He sung of Robin's love for little Jenny Wren;
And when he came unto the end, then he began again.

The Bulfinch walked by Robin, and thus to him did say,
"Pray, mark, friend Robin Redbreast, that Goldfinch dressed so gay;

What though her gay apparel becomes her very well;
Yet Jenny's modest dress and look must bear away the bell!"

Then came the bride and bridegroom; quite plainly was she dressed;
And blushed so much, her cheeks were as red as Robin's breast.

But Robin cheered her up: "My pretty Jen," said he,
"We're going to be married, and happy we shall be."

The Goldfinch came on next, to give away the bride;
The Linnet, being bridesmaid, walked by Jenny's side.

And, as she was a-walking, said "Upon my word,
I think that your Cock Robin is a very pretty bird."

"And will you have her, Robin, to be your wedded wife?"
"Yes, I will," says Robin, "and love her all my life."

"And you will have him, Jenny, your husband now to be?"
"Yes, I will," says Jenny, "and love him heartily."

The Blackbird and the Thrush, and charming Nightingale,
Whose sweet "jug" sweetly echoes through every grove and dale;—

The Sparrow and Tomtit, and many more were there;
All came to see the wedding of Jenny Wren the fair.

"O, then," says Parson Rook, "who gives this maid away?"
"I do," says the Goldfinch, "and her fortune I will pay;—
"Here's a bag of grain of many sorts, and other things beside.
Now happy be the bridegroom, and happy be the bride!"

Then on her finger fair, Cock Robin put the ring;
"You're married now," says Parson Rook; while the Lark
    aloud did sing,—
"Happy be the bridegroom, and happy be the bride!
And may not man, nor bird, nor beast, this happy pair divide."

The birds were asked to dine; not Jenny's friends alone,
But every pretty songster that had Cock Robin known.

They had a cherry-pie, besides some currant-wine,
And every guest brought something, that sumptuous they might dine.

Now they all sat or stood, to eat and drink;
And every one said what he happened to think.

They each took a bumper, and drank to the pair;
Cock Robin the bridegroom, and Jenny Wren the fair.

The dinner things removed, they all began to sing;
And soon they made the place near a mile around to ring.

The concert it was fine; and every bird tried
Who best should sing for Robin, and Jenny Wren the bride.

When in came the Cuckoo, and made a great rout;
He caught hold of Jenny, and pulled her about.

Cock Robin was angry, and so was the Sparrow,
Who fetched in a hurry his bow and his arrow.

His aim then he took, but he took it not right;
His skill was not good, or he shot in a fright;

For the Cuckoo he missed,—but Cock Robin he killed!
And all the birds mourned that his blood was so spilled.

AN OLD WOMAN
WAS SWEEPING HER HOUSE

An old woman was sweeping her house, and she found a little crooked sixpence. "What," said she, "shall I do with this little sixpence? I will go to market, and buy a little pig." As she was coming home, she came to a stile; the piggy would not go over the stile.

She went a little further, and she met a dog. So she said to the dog, "Dog! bite pig; piggy won't go over the stile; and I shan't get home to-night." But the dog would not.

She went a little further, and she met a stick. So she said, "Stick! stick! beat dog; dog won't bite pig; piggy won't get over the stile; and I shan't get home to-night." But the stick would not.

She went a little further, and she met a fire. So she said, "Fire! fire! burn stick; stick won't beat dog; dog won't bite pig" (and so forth, always repeating the foregoing words). But the fire would not.

She went a little further, and she met some water. So she said, "Water! water! quench fire; fire won't burn stick," etc. But the water would not.

She went a little further, and she met an ox. So she said, "Ox! ox! drink water; water won't quench fire," etc. But the ox would not.

She went a little further, and she met a butcher. So she said, "Butcher! butcher! kill ox; ox won't drink water," etc. But the butcher would not.

She went a little further, and she met a rope. So she said, "Rope! rope! hang butcher; butcher won't kill ox," etc. But the rope would not.

She went a little further, and she met a rat. So she said, "Rat, rat! gnaw rope; rope won't hang butcher," etc. But the rat would not.

She went a little further, and she met a cat. So she said, "Cat! cat! kill rat; rat won't gnaw rope," etc. But the cat said to her, "If you will go to yonder cow, and fetch me a saucer of milk, I will kill the rat." So away went the old woman to the cow.

But the cow said to her, "If you will go to yonder haystack, and fetch me a handful of hay, I'll give you the milk." So away went the old woman to the haystack; and she brought the hay to the cow.

As soon as the cow had eaten the hay, she gave the old woman the milk; so away she went with it in a saucer to the cat.

As soon as the cat had lapped up the milk, the cat began to kill the rat; the rat began to gnaw the rope; the rope began to hang the butcher; the butcher began to kill the ox; the ox began to drink the water; the water began to quench the fire; the fire began to burn the stick; the stick began to beat the dog; the dog began to bite the pig; the little pig in a fright jumped over the stile; and so the old woman got home that night.

THREE LITTLE KITTENS

Three little kittens lost their mittens,
  and they began to cry,
  Oh! mother dear,
  We very much fear
  That we have lost our mittens.
Lost your mittens! You naughty kittens!
  Then you shall have no pie.
  Mee-ow, mee-ow, mee-ow.
  No, you shall have no pie.
  Mee-ow, mee-ow, mee-ow.
The three little kittens found their mittens,
  and they began to cry,
  Oh! mother dear,
  See here, see here!
  See, we have found our mittens.
Put on your mittens, you silly kittens,
  and you shall have some pie.
Purr-r, purr-r, purr-r,
  Oh! let us have the pie!
  Purr-r, purr-r, purr-r.

BOW-WOW

Bow-wow, says the dog;
   Mew-mew, says the cat;
Grunt, grunt, says the hog;
   And squeak, goes the rat.

Tu-whu, says the owl;
   Caw, caw, says the crow;
Quack, quack, says the duck;
   And what sparrows say you know.

So, with sparrows, and owls;
   With rats and with dogs;
With ducks and with crows;
   With cats and with hogs,

A charming song I have made,
   To please you, my dear;
And if it's well sung,
   'Twill be charming to hear.

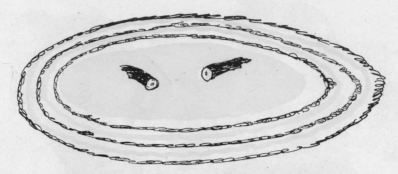

THERE WERE TWO CATS

There were two cats of Kilkenny,
Each thought there was one cat too many,
So they fought and they fit,
And they scratched and they bit,
Till, excepting their nails and the tips of their tails,
Instead of two cats there weren't any.

COME DANCE A JIG

Come, dance a jig
To my granny's pig,
With a rawdy, rowdy, dowdy;
Come dance a jig
To my granny's pig,
And pussy-cat shall crowdy.

THREE BLIND MICE

Three blind mice, see how they run!
They all ran after the farmer's wife,
Who cut off their tails with the carving-knife,
Did you ever see such fools in your life?
Three blind mice.

TWO LITTLE DOGS

Two little dogs were basking in the cinders,
Two cats were playing in the windows,
When two little mice popped out of a hole,
And up to a fine piece of cheese they stole.
The two little dogs cried, "Cheese is nice!"
But the two little cats jumped down in a trice,
And cracked the bones of the two little mice.

THERE WERE THREE
JOVIAL HUNTSMEN

There were three jovial huntsmen,
 As I have heard them say,
And they would go a-hunting
 Upon St. David's day.

All the day they hunted,
 And nothing could they find
But a ship a-sailing,
 A-sailing with the wind.

One said it was a ship,
 The other he said, "Nay;"
The third said it was a house,
 With the chimney blown away.

And all the night they hunted,
 And nothing could they find
But the moon a-gliding,
 A-gliding with the wind.

One said it was the moon,
 The other he said, "Nay;"
The third said it was a cheese,
 With half o't cut away.

The first said it was a hare,
    The second he said, "Nay;"
The third said it was a calf,
    And the cow had run away.

And all the day they hunted,
    And nothing could they find
But an owl in a holly-tree,
    And that they left behind.

One said it was an owl,
    The other he said, "Nay;"
The third said 'twas an old man,
    And his beard growing gray.

All the day they hunted,
    And nothing could they find
But a hedgehog in a bramble-bush,
    And that they left behind.

The first said it was a hedgehog,
    The second he said, "Nay;"
The third it was a pin-cushion,
    And the pins stuck in wrong way.

And all the night they hunted,
    And nothing could they find
But a hare in a turnip-field,
    And that they left behind.

"COO, COO, WHAT SHALL I DO?"

The dove says, "Coo, coo, what shall I do?
I can scarce maintain two."
"Pooh, pooh," says the wren, "I have got ten,
And keep them all like gentlemen!"

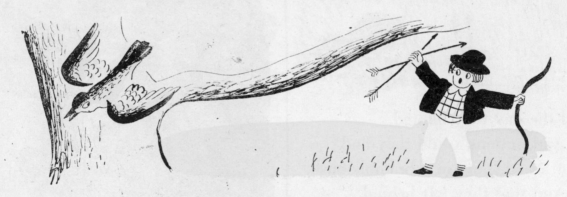

A LITTLE COCK-SPARROW

A little cock-sparrow sat on a tree,
Looking as happy as happy could be,
Till a boy came by with his bow and arrow,
Says he, "I will shoot the little cock-sparrow.

"His body will make a nice little stew,
And his giblets will make me a little pie, too."
Says the little cock-sparrow, "I'll be shot if I stay,"
So he clapped his wings, and flew away.

BA-A BA-A BLACK SHEEP

Ba-a, ba-a, black sheep, have you any wool?
Yes, sir, yes, sir, three bags full:
One for my master, one for my dame,
But none for the little boy who cries in the lane.

THERE WERE TWO BIRDS

There were two birds sat on a stone,
    Fal la, la la lal de,
One flew away, and then there was one,
    Fal la, la la lal de,
The other flew after, and then there was none,
    Fal la, la la lal de,
And so the poor stone was left all alone,
    Fal la, la la lal de.

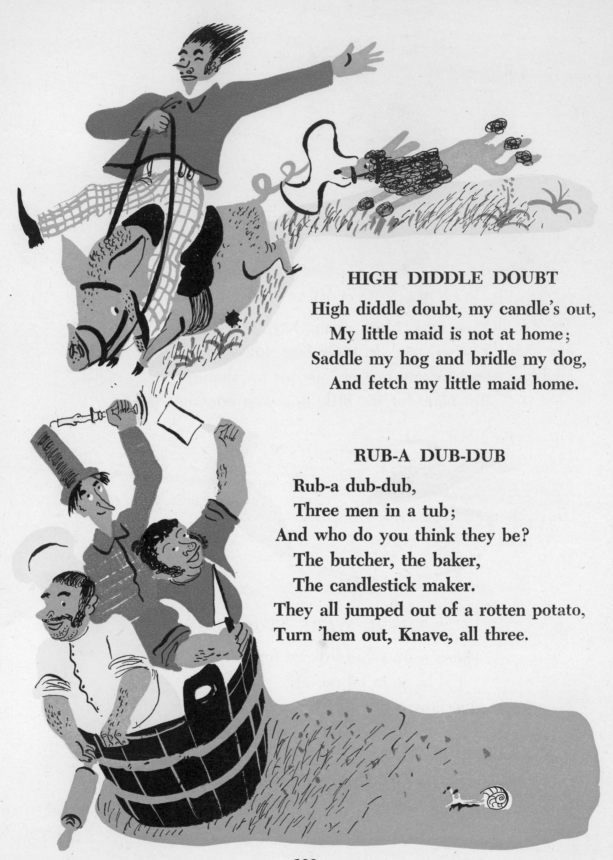

HIGH DIDDLE DOUBT

High diddle doubt, my candle's out,
    My little maid is not at home;
Saddle my hog and bridle my dog,
    And fetch my little maid home.

RUB-A DUB-DUB

Rub-a dub-dub,
    Three men in a tub;
And who do you think they be?
    The butcher, the baker,
    The candlestick maker.
They all jumped out of a rotten potato,
Turn 'hem out, Knave, all three.

DICKERY, DICKERY, DARE

Dickery, dickery, dare,
The pig flew up in the air;
The man in brown soon brought him down,
Dickery, dickery, dare.

THE JOLLY MILLER

There was a jolly miller
   Lived on the river Dee:
He worked and sang from morn till night,
   No lark so blithe as he.

And this the burden of his song
   For ever used to be—
"I care for nobody—no! not I,
   Since nobody cares for me."

CROSS-PATCH
DRAW THE LATCH

Cross-patch,
Draw the latch,
Sit by the fire and spin;
Take a cup
And drink it up,
And call your neighbors in.

MULTIPLICATION

Multiplication is vexation,
Division is as bad;
The Rule of Three doth puzzle me,
And Practice drives me mad.

GIDDY GIRLS, NOISY BOYS

Giddy girls, noisy boys,
Come and buy me painted toys;
Medals made of gingerbread,
And penny horses white and red.

IF WISHES WERE HORSES

If wishes were horses,
Beggars might ride;
If turnips were watches,
I would wear one by my side.

AS I WALKED BY MYSELF

As I walked by myself
And talked to myself,
Myself said unto me:
Look to thyself,
Take care of thyself,
For nobody cares for thee.

I answered myself
And said to myself
In the self-same repartee:
Look to thyself
Or not look to thyself,
The self-same thing will be.

BOBBY SHAFTOE

Bobby Shaftoe's gone to sea,
Silver buckles at his knee;
He'll come back and marry me,—
Pretty Bobby Shaftoe!

Bobby Shaftoe's fat and fair,
Combing down his yellow hair,
He's my love for evermair,—
Pretty Bobby Shaftoe!

A DILLAR, A DOLLAR

A dillar, a dollar,
A ten o'clock scholar,
What makes you come so soon?
You used to come at ten o'clock,
And now you come at noon.

HOT-CROSS BUNS!

Hot-cross Buns!
Old woman runs!
One a penny, two a penny,
Hot-cross Buns.

If you have no daughters,
Give them to your sons.
One a penny, two a penny,
Hot-cross Buns.

TOM, TOM, THE PIPER'S SON

Tom, Tom, the piper's son,
Stole a pig, and away he run.
The pig was eat, and Tom was beat,
And Tom went crying down the
    street.

IF A MAN WHO TURNIP CRIES

If a man who turnips cries,
Cries not when his father dies,
It is a proof that he would rather
Have a turnip than his father.

109

THERE WAS A CROOKED MAN

There was a crooked man, and he went a crooked mile;
He found a crooked sixpence against a crooked stile;
He bought a crooked cat, which caught a crooked mouse,
And they all lived together in a little crooked house.

INDEX